# The Thinking Tre

# HOMESCHOOLING
## With
# DOLPHINS

## STUDY SIX SUBJECTS
## FUN-SCHOOLING CURRICULUM

### 180 Lessons & Activities For Dolphin Lovers of all Ages!

By: Notika Pashenko & Sarah Janisse Brown

We use the Dyslexie Font by Christian Boer

The Thinking Tree Publishing Company, LLC

# FUNSCHOOLINGBOOKS.COM

# THIS CURRICULUM COVERS:

## SUBJECTS

- Language Arts
- Science
- Geography
- Social Studies
- Math Time
- Art & Drawing

## ACTIVITIES:

- Projects & Experiments
- Environmental Studies
- Documentaries
- Research & Library Skills
- Audio Books
- Conservation
- Cursive Writing
- Reading & Spelling
- Creative Writing
- Logic, Comics & Mazes

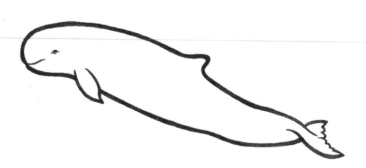

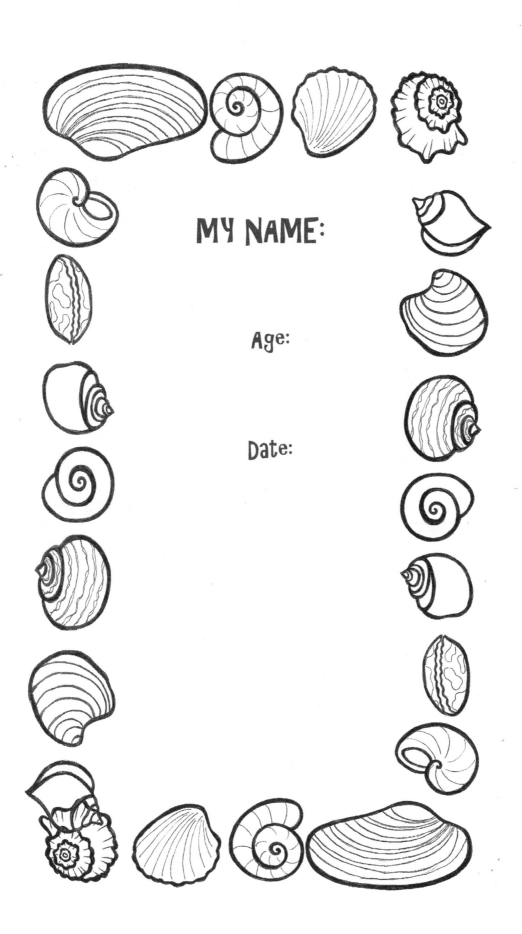

MY NAME:

Age:

Date:

# INSTRUCTIONS
## CHOOSE YOUR TOPICS!

What do you want to know

about Dolphins and Ocean Life?

Draw **FIVE** things you are curious about:

# ACTION STEPS:

1. Go to the library or bookstore.

2. Bring home a stack of at least FIVE interesting books about these topics.

3. Choose some that have diagrams, instructions and illustrations.

4. Choose a book or video series with step-by-step drawing lessons focuses on sea life.

5. Add MATH! Choose any math course to make this a complete curriculum. Use your own math program during Math Time.

# GO TO THE LIBRARY AND CHOOSE FIVE BOOKS TO USE AS SCHOOL BOOKS!

1. Write down the titles on each book cover below.

2. Keep your stack of books in a safe place so you can read a few pages from your books daily.

3. Ask your mom or teacher how many pages to do each day in this Journal. Eight pages a day is best for most kids. Start each day with **A NEW DAY** page.

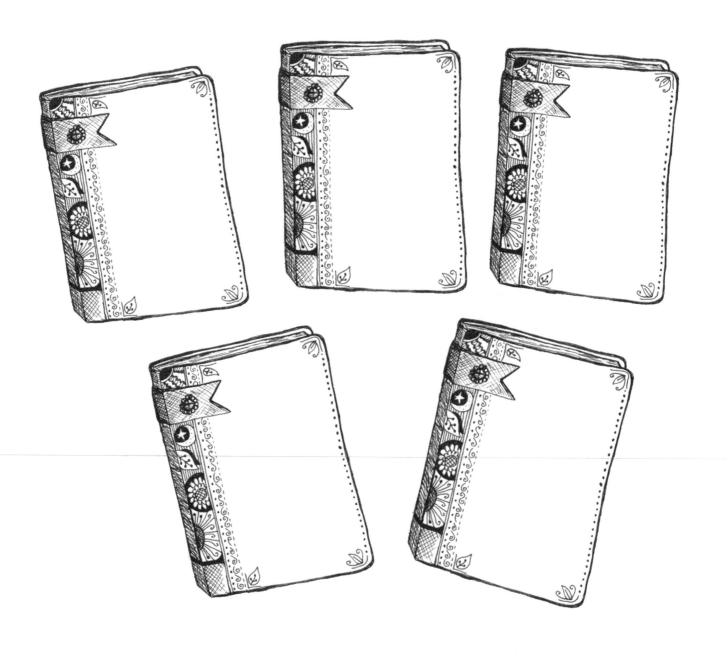

You may choose new books any time.

Flip to the back for more book pages.

Keep all your books in a basket with your pens and pencils.

Have a snack before you start working in this journal.

# PICK OUT NEW BOOKS ANYTIME!
## DRAW THE COVERS HERE:

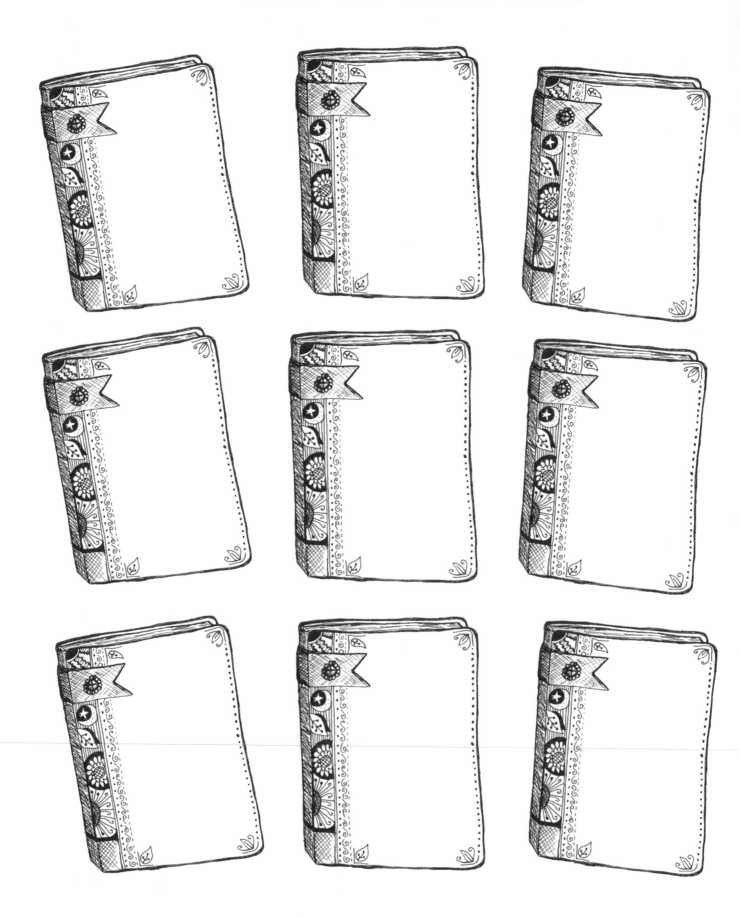

# LEARNING TOOLS

My List of Websites & Research Materials:

_____

_____

_____

_____

_____

_____

_____

_____

_____

_____

_____

_____

_____

_____

_____

## TODAYS DATE:

___ ___ ___

___ ___ ___

___ ___ ___

## TO-DO LIST

1. _____

2. _____

3. _____

4. _____

# A New Day!

## How are you FEELING TODAY?

## I am THANKFUL for:

## Draw a Dolphin Comic:

Some things that go to the trash can be recycled and made into new things to use again! But first, we need to sort them to the right containers.

Today I will
read for

15  30  45  60

MINUTES

**READING TIME**

Write and draw about
what you are reading.

# MOVIE TIME

Watch an Video about Dolphins or the Ocean!

TITLE:_____

RATING:

Using library books research and write the names of the
dolphin's body parts in the boxes.

# ALL ABOUT
# COMMON BOTTLENOSE

## WRITE DOWN THREE FACTS ABOUT THIS ANIMAL:

1._____

_____

2._____

_____

3._____

_____

# RESEARCH & DISCOVERIES

## USE LIBRARY BOOKS, ENCYCLOPEDIAS OR THE INTERNET TO LEARN MORE.

Color the parts of the world where this animal lives.

DRAW MY HOME

DRAW MY FOOD

DRAW MY ENEMIES

## TODAYS DATE:

_ _ _ _ _ _

_ _ _ _ _ _

_ _ _ _ _ _

## TO-DO LIST

1._____

2._____

3._____

4._____

# A New Day!

## How are you FEELING TODAY?

## I am THANKFUL for:

## Draw a Dolphin Comic:

# OCEAN LIFE DRAWING TIME

Use a step-by-step drawing book or video.

# JUST FOR FUN!

# CREATIVE WRITING

Write a short story about these pictures.

_____

_____

_____

_____

_____

_____

_____

_____

_____

_____

_____

_____

_____

_____

_____

_____

_____

_____

_____

_____

_____

Ask your teacher to help
you decide how many
books to read from each
day.  #_____

READING
TIME

Write and draw about
what you are reading.

# BACKYARD SCIENCE
# NATURE WALK & NATURE STUDY

Draw or write about the things you see outside today.

# SPELLING TIME

Pick a Letter _____

Look in your homeschooling books for

words that start with this letter.

## Write ten spelling words.

1._____

2._____

3._____

4._____

5._____

6._____

7._____

8._____

9._____

10._____

## TODAYS DATE:

_ _ _ _ _ _ _

_ _ _ _ _ _ _

_ _ _ _ _ _ _

# TO-DO LIST

1._____

2._____

3._____

4._____

# A New Day!

How are you
FEELING TODAY?

I am THANKFUL for:

Draw a Dolphin Comic:

# OCEAN LIFE DRAWING TIME

Use a step-by-step drawing book or video.

# MOVIE TIME

Watch an Video about Dolphins or the Ocean!

TITLE:_____

RATING:

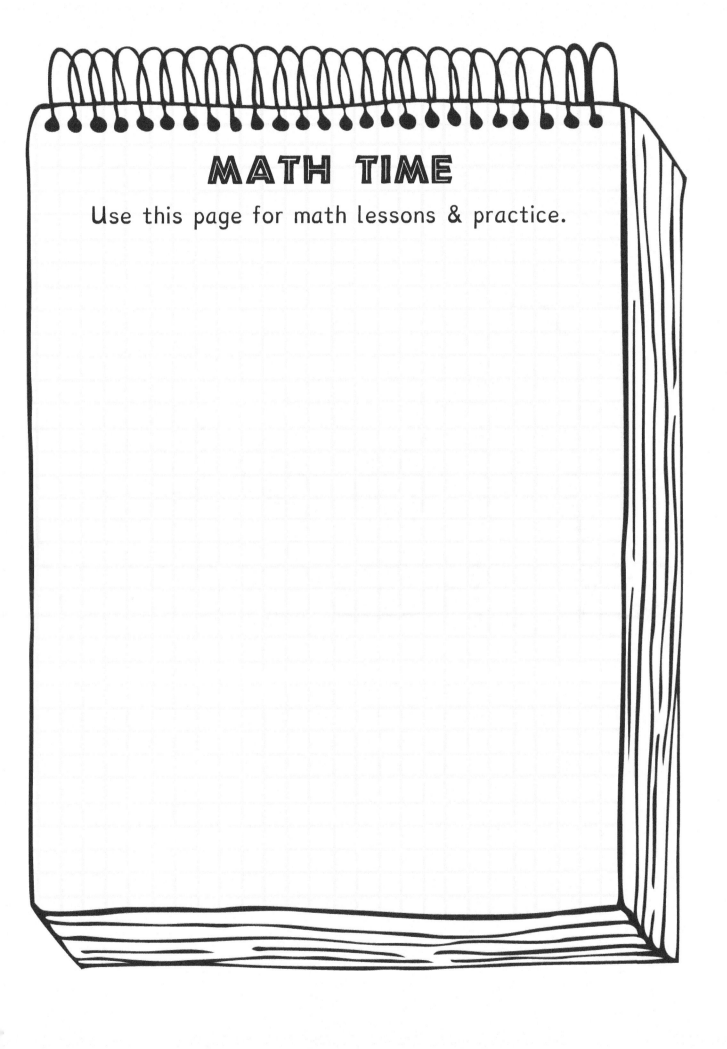

# MATH TIME

Use this page for math lessons & practice.

# Water Filter eXperiment

YOU WILL Need:

PLastic bottLe, Sand, SMall rocks, Cotton, SMall piece oF cloth, Scissors, Dirty Water, eLastic.

Many dolphins are classified as endangered species. One of the things that threaten these dolphins is water pollution. Water in rivers is neither clean enough for dolphins nor humans. Before we can use the water in our homes it goes through many levels of filtration and treatment.
  This experiment will help us see how the first level of filtration works.
Water from a river or lake can be used for experiment or you can just mix some mud and dirt in clean water.

## INSTRUCTIONS:

Cut the bottle in half or ask an adult to do it for you. Remove the bottle cap and tie a folded piece of cloth around the

opening, using an elastic or a string. Then put layers of cotton, sand and small pebbles. Slowly pour the dirty water through the

filter you just created.

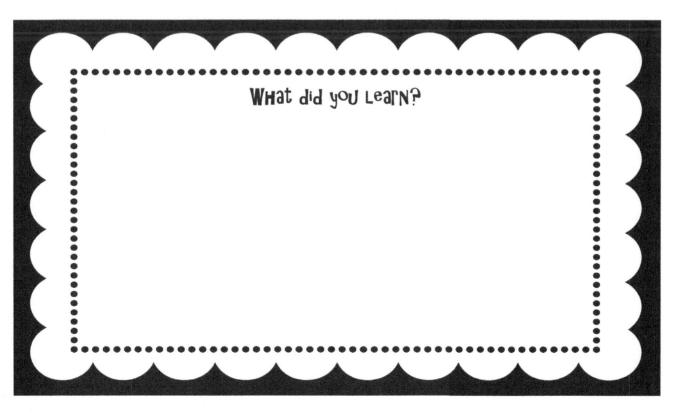

WHAT did yoU LearN?

# ALL ABOUT

# HUMPBACK DOLPHIN

## WRITE DOWN THREE FACTS ABOUT THIS ANIMAL:

1._____

_____

2._____

_____

3._____

_____

# RESEARCH & DISCOVERIES

## USE LIBRARY BOOKS, ENCYCLOPEDIAS OR THE INTERNET TO LEARN MORE.

Color the parts of the world where this animal lives.

| DRAW MY HOME | DRAW MY FOOD | DRAW MY ENEMIES |
| --- | --- | --- |
| | | |

## TODAYS DATE:

_ _ _ _ _

_ _ _ _ _

_ _ _ _ _

## TO-DO LIST

1._____

2._____

3._____

4._____

# A New Day!

How are you
FEELING TODAY?

I am THANKFUL for:

Draw a Dolphin Comic:

# LISTENING TIME

## CLASSICAL MUSIC, HISTORY & LITERATURE

Listen to Story of the World, an audio book or classical music. Draw and doodle below.

I am listening to: _____

# Freezing eXperiMent

Water, SaLt, MeaSuriNg SpooNS, 3 Freezer SaFe cups.

Some parts of the ocean are freezing cold and have ice on the surface, but they never freeze all the way through. Let's conduct an experiment to discover why this is happening.

## Instructions:

Pour water in three small cups. One cup will contain plain water. Mix a table spoon of salt in the second cup. Mix three table spoons of salt in the third cup. You may mark your cups with stickers or color papers.

Now put your cups in the freezer. Check them after 15 minutes, 30 minutes, after an hour. What did you notice?

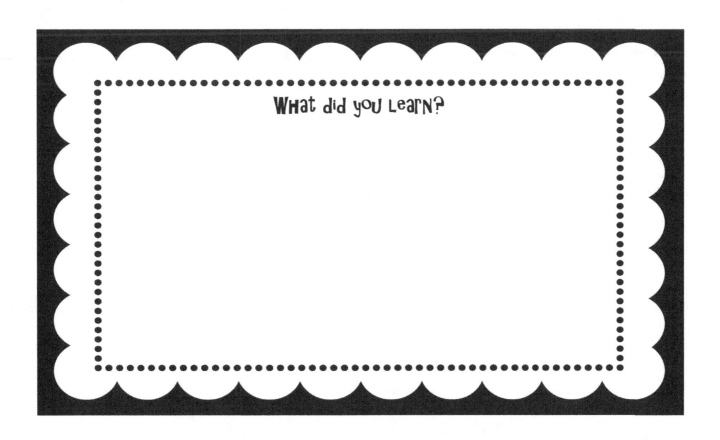

What did you Learn?

CREATE A COMIC STRIP

CURSIVE WRITING PRACTICE

# COLORING TIME

## Relax & Listen to an Audio Book

# DRAWING TIME

## PRACTICE DRAWING DOLPHINS & SEA CREATURES

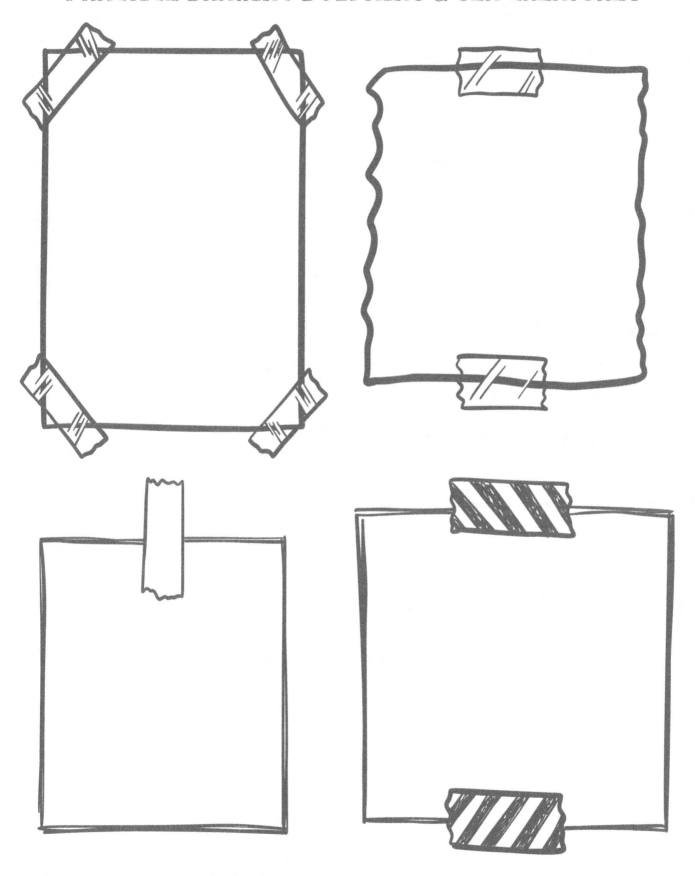

## TODAYS DATE:

_ _ _ _ _ _ _

_ _ _ _ _ _ _

_ _ _ _ _ _ _

## TO-DO LIST

1._____

2._____

3._____

4._____

## A New Day!

## How are you FEELING TODAY?

## I am THANKFUL for:

## Draw a Dolphin Comic:

# LISTENING TIME

## CLASSICAL MUSIC, HISTORY & LITERATURE

Listen to Story of the World, an audio book

or classical music. Draw and doodle below.

I am listening to: _____

# CREATIVE WRITING

Write a short story about these pictures.

_____

_____

_____

_____

_____

_____

_____

_____

_____

_____

_____

_____

_____

_____

_____

_____

_____

_____

_____

_____

Today I will
read for

15  30  45  60

MINUTES

# READING
## TIME

Write and draw about
what you are reading.

# BACKYARD SCIENCE
# NATURE WALK & NATURE STUDY

Draw or write about the things you see outside today.

# MOVIE TIME

Watch an Video about Dolphins or the Ocean!

TITLE:_____

RATING:

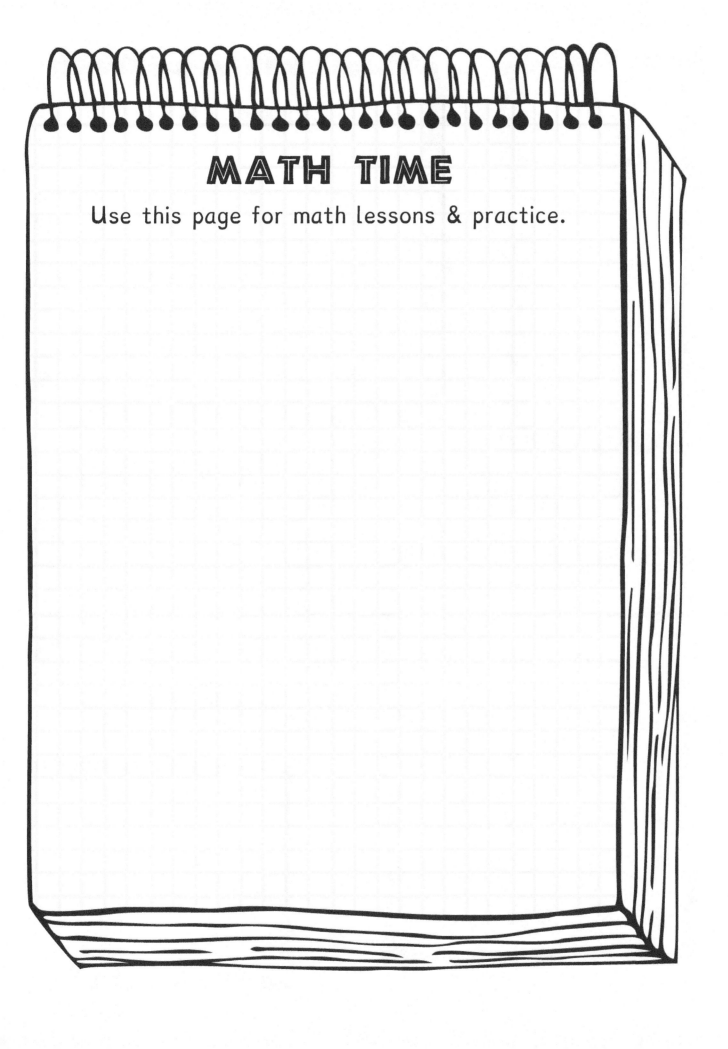

# MATH TIME

Use this page for math lessons & practice.

## TODAYS DATE:

- - - - - -

- - - - - -

- - - - - -

## TO-DO LIST

1._____

2._____

3._____

4._____

# A New Day!

How are you
FEELING TODAY?

I am THANKFUL for:

Draw a Dolphin Comic:

# COLORING TIME

## Relax & Listen to an Audio Book

# ALL ABOUT

# RISSOS  DOLPHIN

## WRITE DOWN THREE FACTS ABOUT THIS ANIMAL:

1._____

_____

2._____

_____

3._____

_____

# RESEARCH & DISCOVERIES

## USE LIBRARY BOOKS, ENCYCLOPEDIAS OR THE INTERNET TO LEARN MORE.

Color the parts of the world where this animal lives.

| DRAW MY HOME | DRAW MY FOOD | DRAW MY ENEMIES |
| --- | --- | --- |
| | | |

# Solar puriFication eXperiment

You Will Need:

Dirty Water, Large boWL, Small glaSS, Small rock, plastic Wrap or a plastic bag, thread..

There are many ways to purify water. One of the ways is to use the power of the sun. When water is heated up by the sun it turns into vapor that rises up, leaving the dirt or salt behind. In nature the water that rises up, gets collected in the clouds and falls down as rain.

## INSTRUCTIONS:

Place the small glass inside the bowl. Pour dirty water into the bowl or you can use clean water mixed with salt. Make sure the water does not get into the glass. Cover the bowl with a plastic wrap or plastic bag and secure it with a thread or tape. Carefully place a small rock right above the glass. Keep the bowl out on a warm sunny day. Check the cup after a few hours.

What did you Learn?

## READING TIME

Write and draw about what you are reading.

## TODAYS DATE:

_ _ _ _ _ _

_ _ _ _ _ _

_ _ _ _ _ _

## TO-DO LIST

1. _____

2. _____

3. _____

4. _____

# A New Day!

How are you
FEELING TODAY?

I am THANKFUL for:

Draw a Dolphin Comic:

# BACKYARD SCIENCE
## NATURE WALK & NATURE STUDY

Draw or write about the things you see outside today.

# Amazon river dolphin

## WRITE DOWN THREE FACTS ABOUT THIS ANIMAL:

1._____

_____

2._____

_____

3._____

_____

# RESEARCH & DISCOVERIES
## USE LIBRARY BOOKS, ENCYCLOPEDIAS OR THE INTERNET TO LEARN MORE.

Write the names of the rivers where this animal lives.

Draw my home

Draw my food

Draw my enemies

# SPELLING TIME

Pick a Letter _____

Look in your homeschooling books for

words that start with this letter.

Write ten spelling words.

1._____

2._____

3._____

4._____

5._____

6._____

7._____

8._____

9._____

10._____

# MOVIE TIME

Watch an Video about Dolphins or the Ocean!

TITLE:_____

Draw Your Favorite Scenes:

RATING:

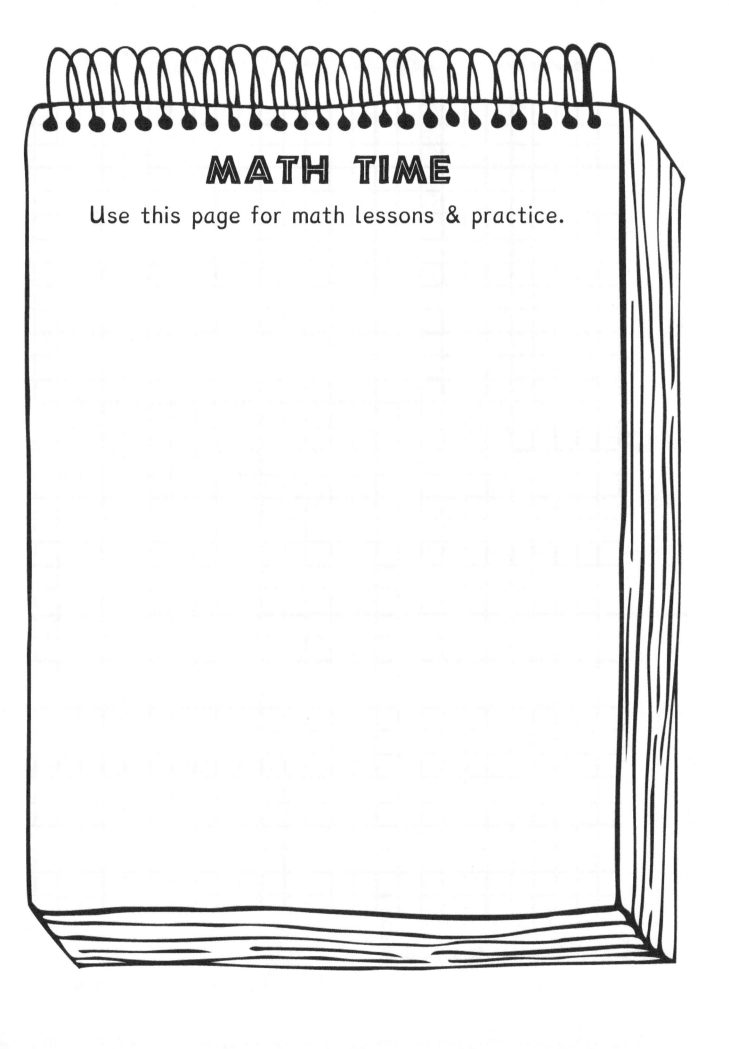

# MATH TIME

Use this page for math lessons & practice.

## TODAYS DATE:

_ _ _ _ _ _

_ _ _ _ _ _

_ _ _ _ _ _

## TO-DO LIST

1._____

2._____

3._____

4._____

# A New Day!

How are you
FEELING TODAY?

I am THANKFUL for:

Draw a Dolphin Comic:

# BACKYARD SCIENCE
# NATURE WALK & NATURE STUDY

Draw or write about the things you see outside today.

Today I will read for

15 30 45 60

MINUTES

READING TIME

Write and draw about what you are reading.

# COPYWORK

Copy a sentence from one of your library books.

TITLE: _____

Page#_____

_____

_____

_____

_____

_____

# DRAWING TIME

Copy an illustration from one of your books.

# ALL ABOUT

# HOURGLASS DOLPHIN

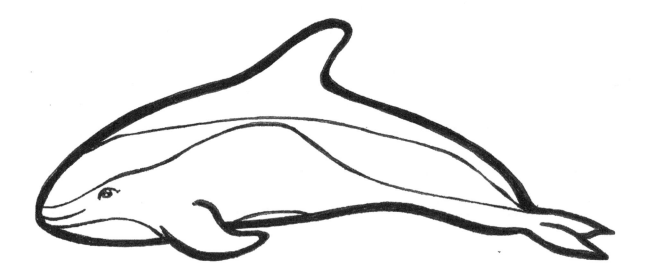

## WRITE DOWN THREE FACTS ABOUT THIS ANIMAL:

1._____

_____

2._____

_____

3._____

_____

# RESEARCH & DISCOVERIES

## USE LIBRARY BOOKS, ENCYCLOPEDIAS OR THE INTERNET TO LEARN MORE.

Color the parts of the world where this animal lives.

| DRAW MY HOME | DRAW MY FOOD | DRAW MY ENEMIES |
| --- | --- | --- |
|  |  |  |

CREATE A COMIC STRIP

CURSIVE WRITING PRACTICE

## TODAYS DATE:

------

------

------

# TO-DO LIST

1._____

2._____

3._____

4._____

# A New Day!

How are you
FEELING TODAY?

I am THANKFUL for:

Draw a Dolphin Comic:

# Reduce, Reuse, Recycle

Recycling is when we reprocess used items and waste to make useful products out of this material once again.

Glass, paper, plastic and metal are some commonly recycled materials.

Choose two of these materials: one for each box below. In the boxes, draw some common items that can be recycled.

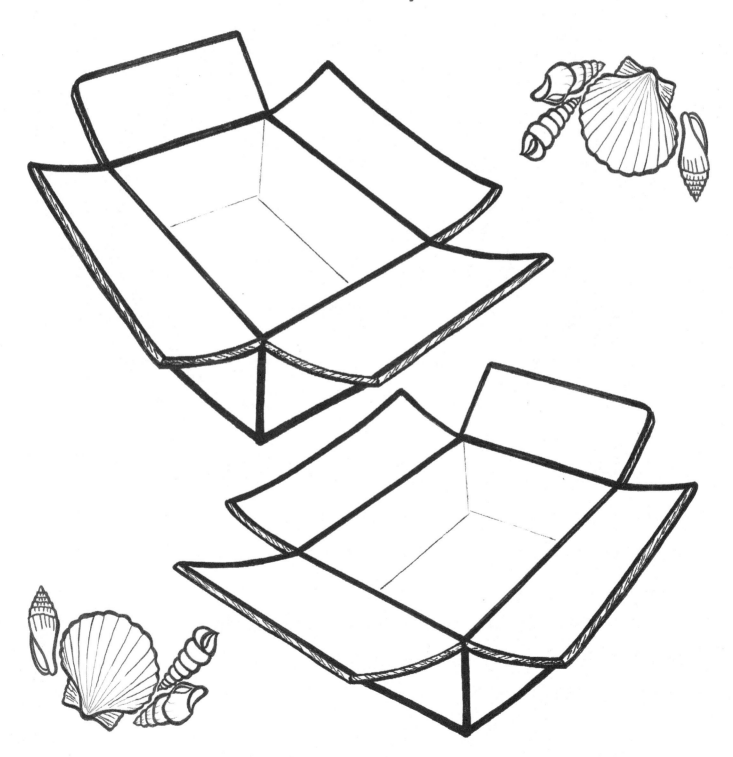

# LandFill eXperiment

YoU WiLL Need:

A Big WooDeN branch, HaMMer aNd NaiLS or a rope, SoMe plastic aNd paper Wrappers and Food Waste iteMS.

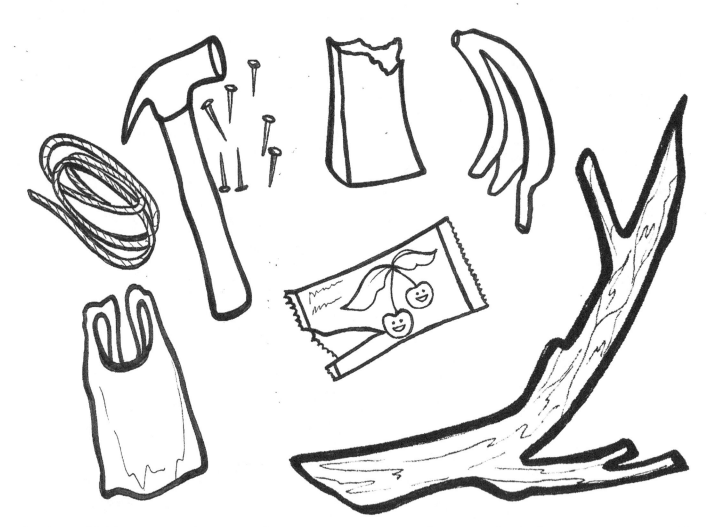

A landfill is a place where waste is dumped. Waste is usually buried in landfills. Landfills smell and look bad. They can produce dangerous gases and pollute air, water and soil. Landfills harm plants and animals. Let us conduct an experiment to see what happens with the waste, once it is buried under ground!

## INSTRUCTIONS:

Choose a big wooden branch and a few different pieces of waste. Make sure they are all made of different materials: paper, plastic, foil, cardboard, vegetable or fruit peels... Ask an adult to nail your waste items to a branch or tie them with a synthetic rope. Dig a hole in a soil and burry the branch. Note down the location. Check on your branch after a week and again after two weeks.

WHAT did yoU LearN?

# MOVIE TIME

Watch an Video about Dolphins or the Ocean!

TITLE:_____

RATING:

Draw Your Favorite Scenes:

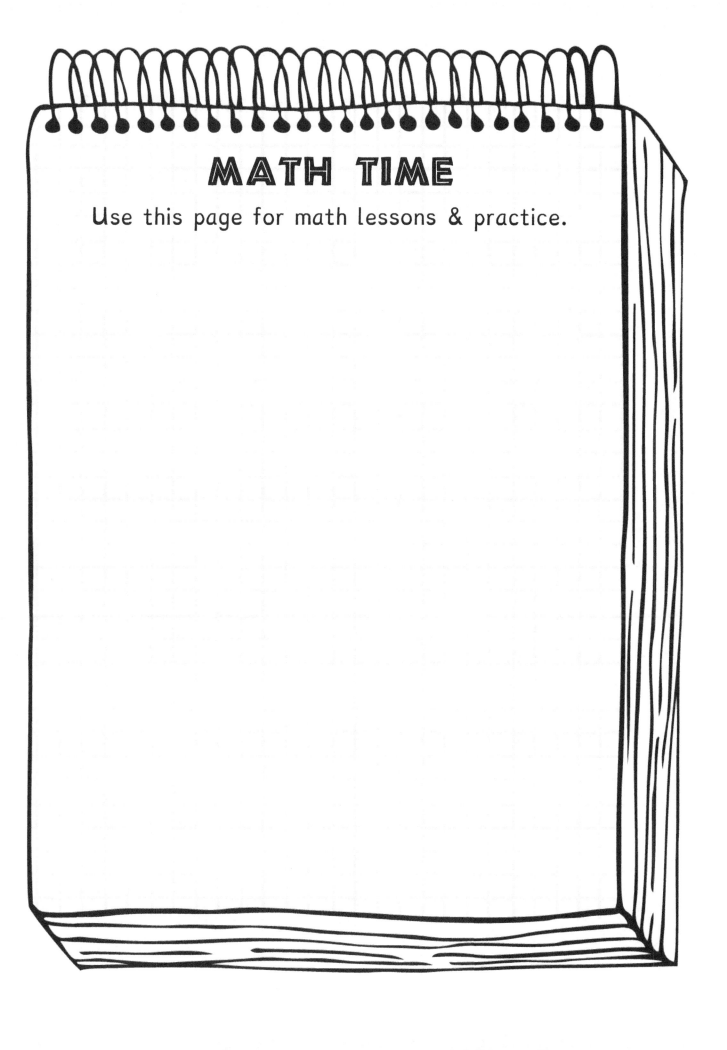

# MATH TIME

Use this page for math lessons & practice.

# DRAWING TIME

## PRACTICE DRAWING DOLPHINS & SEA CREATURES

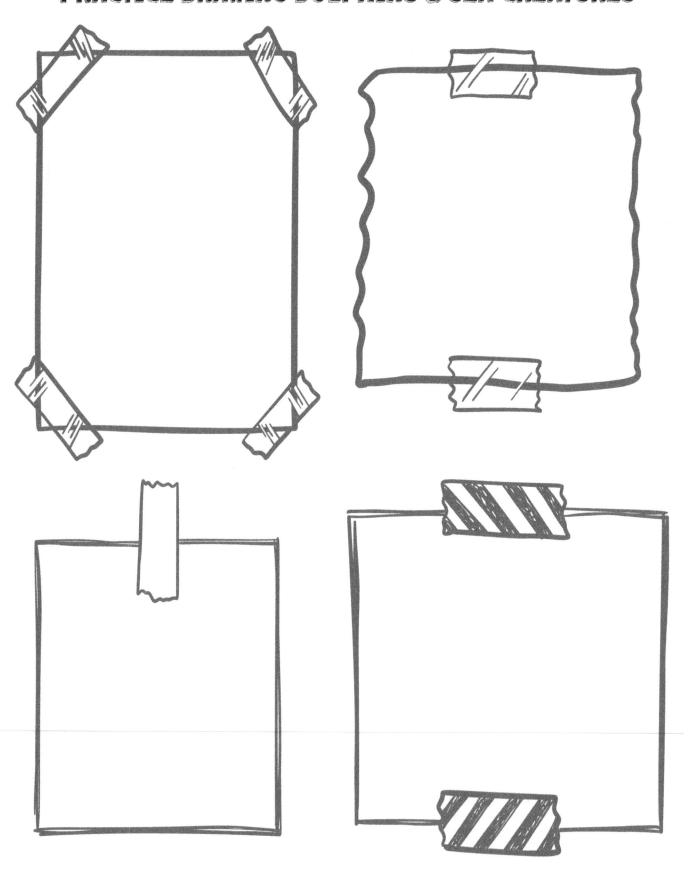

## TODAYS DATE:

_ _ _ _ _ _

_ _ _ _ _ _

_ _ _ _ _ _

## TO-DO LIST

1._____

2._____

3._____

4._____

# A New Day!

## How are you FEELING TODAY?

I am THANKFUL for:

Draw a Dolphin Comic:

# ALL ABOUT

# RIGHT WHALE DOLPHIN

## WRITE DOWN THREE FACTS ABOUT THIS ANIMAL:

1._____

_____

2._____

_____

3._____

_____

# RESEARCH & DISCOVERIES

## USE LIBRARY BOOKS, ENCYCLOPEDIAS OR THE INTERNET TO LEARN MORE.

Color the parts of the world where this animal lives.

| DRAW MY HOME | DRAW MY FOOD | DRAW MY ENEMIES |
| --- | --- | --- |
|  |  |  |

READING
TIME

Write and draw about
what you are reading.

# BACKYARD SCIENCE
## NATURE WALK & NATURE STUDY

Draw or write about the things you see outside today.

# Composting Jar Experiment

Glass jar, elastic or a thread, piece of cheese cloth or cotton cloth, food waste, paper waste or dry leaves, little bit of soil.

Compost is a type of fertilizer that is made from plants and vegetable waste. The vegetable waste is broken down by germs and made into compost. Composting is a very good way to process waste. To start a compost pile in the garden a special container or a trench in the ground can be used. Let's

conduct an experiment to see how composting works!

## INSTRUCTIONS:

Fill the jar with waste, alternating layers of food waste and dry leaves or small pieces of paper. You can add a little bit of wet soil. Leave some empty space in the jar for air circulation. Close the jar with the cloth and tie it. Keep it where there is plenty of sunshine and air for best results. It is better to keep the jar outdoors because it can have an unpleasant smell. Check on your jar after a week and again after two weeks.

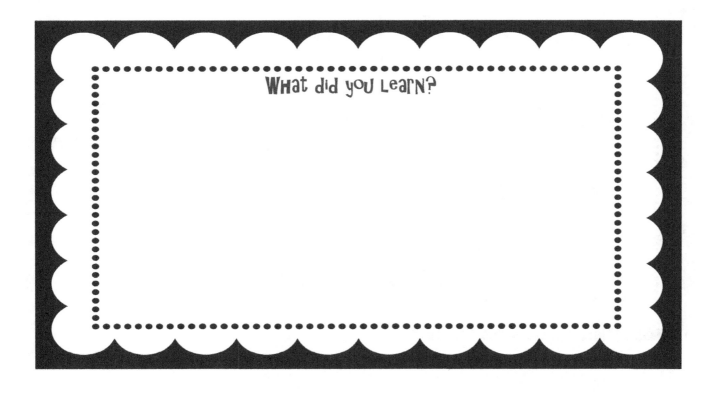

WHat did you Learn?

## TODAYS DATE:

_ _ _ _ _ _

_ _ _ _ _ _

_ _ _ _ _ _

## TO-DO LIST

1._____

2._____

3._____

4._____

# A New Day!

How are you
FEELING TODAY?

I am THANKFUL for:

Draw a Dolphin Comic:

# LISTENING TIME

## CLASSICAL MUSIC, HISTORY & LITERATURE

Listen to Story of the World, an audio book

or classical music. Draw and doodle below.

I am listening to: _____

# CREATIVE WRITING

Write a short story about these pictures.

_____

_____

_____

_____

_____

_____

_____

_____

_____

_____

_____

_____

_____

_____

_____

_____

_____

_____

_____

_____

_____

_____

# MOVIE TIME

Watch an Video about Dolphins or the Ocean!

TITLE:_____

RATING:

Draw Your Favorite Scenes:

# MATH TIME

Use this page for math lessons & practice.

Today I will read for

15 30 45 60

MINUTES

READING TIME

Write and draw about what you are reading.

# OCEAN LIFE DRAWING TIME

Use a step-by-step drawing book or video.

**TODAYS DATE:**

_ _ _ _ _ _ _

_ _ _ _ _ _ _

_ _ _ _ _ _ _

**TO-DO LIST**

1._____

2._____

3._____

4._____

# A New Day!

How are you
FEELING TODAY?

I am THANKFUL for:

Draw a Dolphin Comic:

# Sparkling Ocean bottle

**You Will Need:**

Empty bottle, Water, Food coloring, Sand, Small seashells, rocks and pebbles.

**Instructions:**

Fill the bottle with sand and water. Add some pebbles and seashells. Add a few drops of blue food coloring and mix gently. You can also add sparkles and glitter. Close the jar tightly. Shake gently or flip up and down to see the beautiful designs you made.

Write a list or draw a map of the rivers, lakes and other water bodies that are close to your home.

# ALL ABOUT

# ROUGH-TOOTH DOLPHIN

### WRITE DOWN THREE FACTS ABOUT THIS ANIMAL:

1._____

_____

2._____

_____

3._____

_____

# RESEARCH & DISCOVERIES

## USE LIBRARY BOOKS, ENCYCLOPEDIAS OR THE INTERNET TO LEARN MORE.

Color the parts of the world where this animal lives.

| DRAW MY HOME | DRAW MY FOOD | DRAW MY ENEMIES |
| --- | --- | --- |
| | | |

Today I will
read for
15  30  45  60
MINUTES

READING
TIME

Write and draw about
what you are reading.

# BACKYARD SCIENCE
## NATURE WALK & NATURE STUDY

Draw or write about the things you see outside today.

## TODAYS DATE:

-------

-------

-------

## TO-DO LIST

1._____

2._____

3._____

4._____

# A New Day!

## How are you FEELING TODAY?

## I am THANKFUL for:

## Draw a Dolphin Comic:

# SPELLING TIME

Pick a Letter _____

Look in your homeschooling books for

words that start with this letter.

**Write ten spelling words.**

1._____

2._____

3._____

4._____

5._____

6._____

7._____

8._____

9._____

10._____

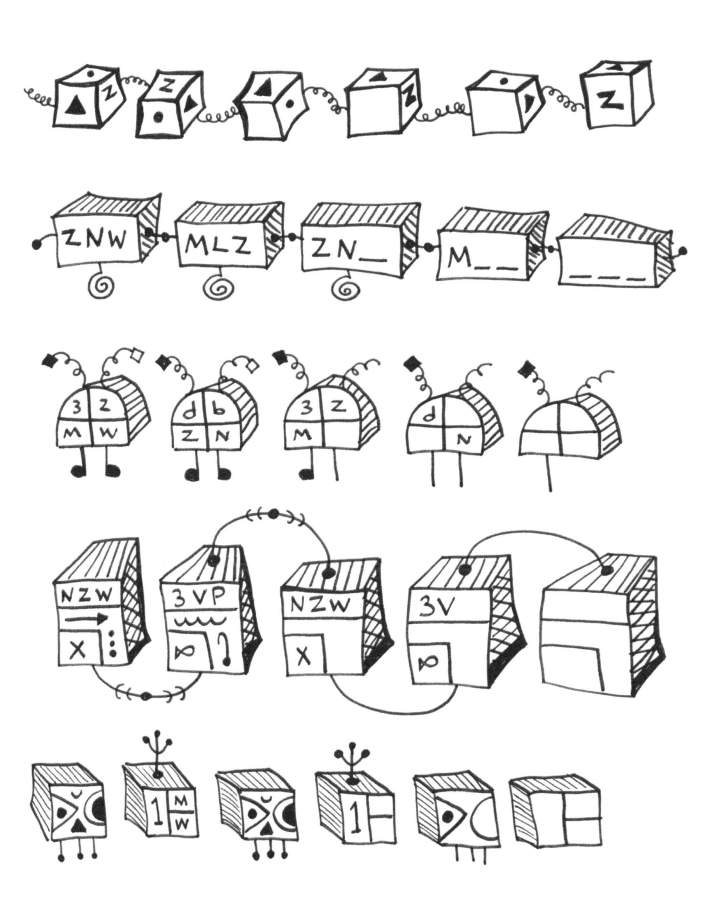

# Bolivian river dolphin

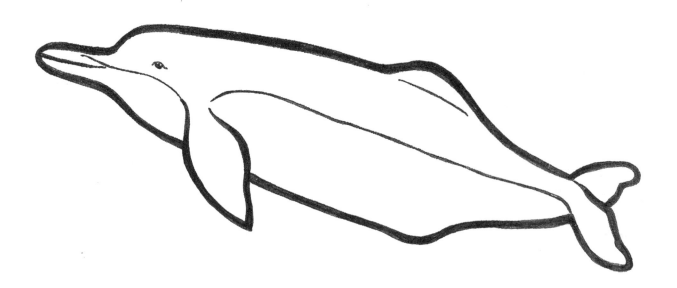

## WRITE DOWN THREE FACTS ABOUT THIS ANIMAL:

1._____

_____

2._____

_____

3._____

_____

# RESEARCH & DISCOVERIES

## USE LIBRARY BOOKS, ENCYCLOPEDIAS OR THE INTERNET TO LEARN MORE.

Write the names of the rivers where this animal lives.

| Draw my home | Draw my food | Draw my enemies |
| --- | --- | --- |
| | | |

CREATE A COMIC STRIP

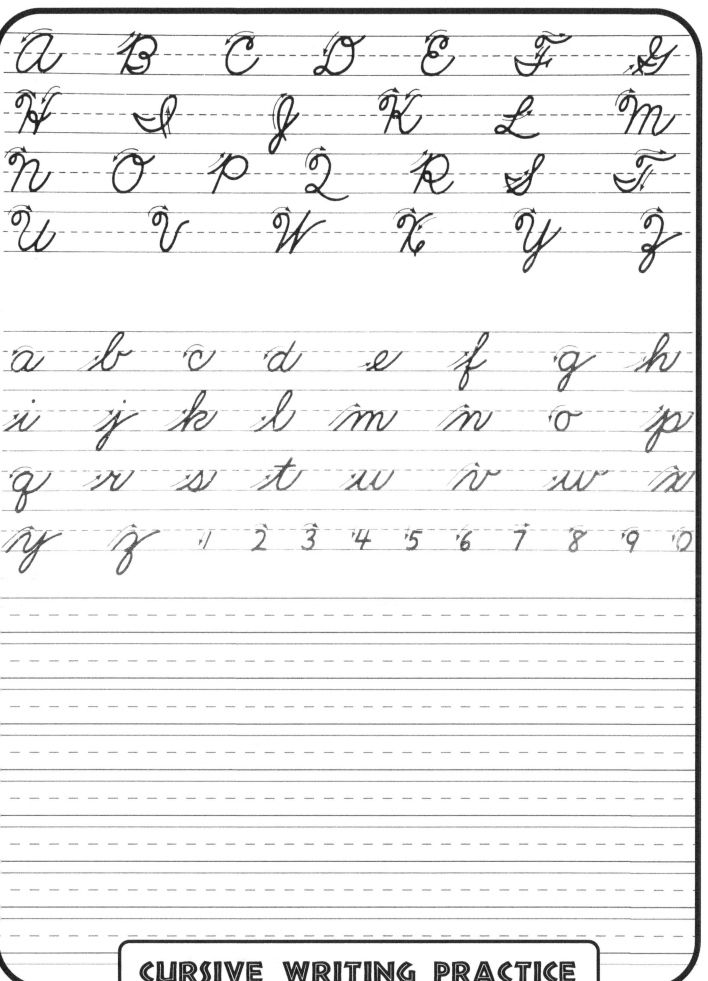

CURSIVE WRITING PRACTICE

**TODAYS DATE:**

------

------

------

# TO-DO LIST

1._____

2._____

3._____

4._____

# A New Day!

How are you
FEELING TODAY?

I am THANKFUL for:

Draw a Dolphin Comic:

# BACKYARD SCIENCE
# NATURE WALK & NATURE STUDY

Draw or write about the things you see outside today.

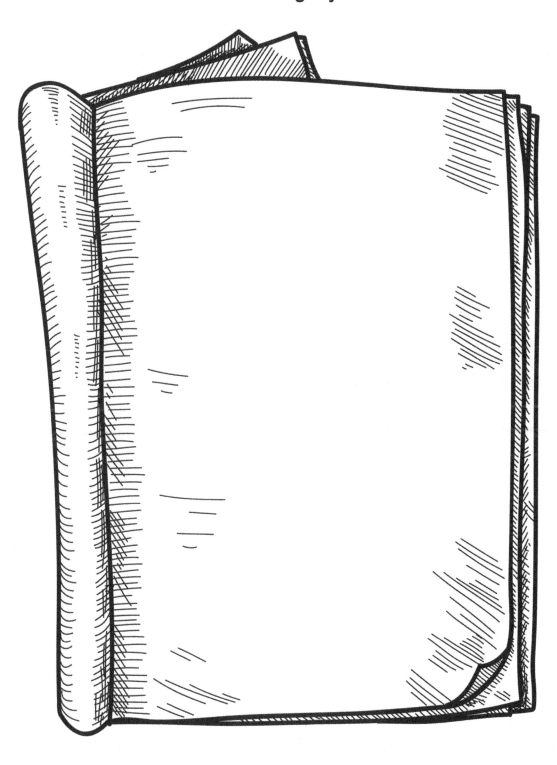

# MOVIE TIME

Watch an Video about Dolphins or the Ocean!

TITLE:_____

RATING:

# MATH TIME

Use this page for math lessons & practice.

# COLORING TIME

## Relax & Listen to an Audio Book

# MATH TIME

Use this page for math lessons & practice.

# ALL ABOUT

# CHILEAN DOLPHIN

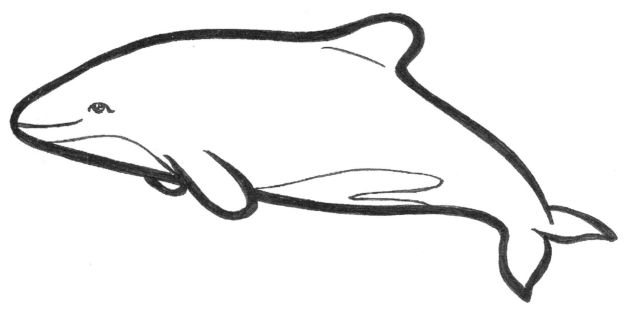

## WRITE DOWN THREE FACTS ABOUT THIS ANIMAL:

1._____

_____

2._____

_____

3._____

_____

# RESEARCH & DISCOVERIES

## USE LIBRARY BOOKS, ENCYCLOPEDIAS OR THE INTERNET TO LEARN MORE.

Color the parts of the world where this animal lives.

| DRAW MY HOME | DRAW MY FOOD | DRAW MY ENEMIES |
|---|---|---|
|  |  |  |

## TODAYS DATE:

_ _ _ _ _ _

_ _ _ _ _ _

_ _ _ _ _ _

## TO-DO LIST

1._____

2._____

3._____

4._____

# A New Day!

### How are you FEELING TODAY?

I am THANKFUL for:

Draw a Dolphin Comic:

# LISTENING TIME

## CLASSICAL MUSIC, HISTORY & LITERATURE

Listen to Story of the World, an audio book

or classical music. Draw and doodle below.

I am listening to: _____

# Making Handmade paper

You will need:

Old newspaper or any waste paper, water, blender, food coloring (optional), bowl, piece of cheese cloth or cotton cloth, wire cooling rack or other sturdy frame, clothespins.

Used paper can be recycled up to 7 times! Paper recycling saves trees, reduces waste and keeps water cleaner. It is very good for the environment. Let us create a piece of recycled paper that can be used to make crafts like bookmarks or handmade cards and learn how recycling works.

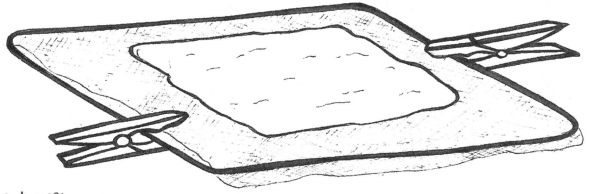

## Instructions:

There is a tool for making paper called paper making mould. You can make a simple alternative of paper making mould by stretching cheesecloth or piece of cotton cloth over a wire cooling rack and securing it with clothespins. Tear paper into small pieces and mix it with warm water. Use a blender to make a fine paste out of your mixture (ask an adult for help). If you don't have a blender, wait for the paper to soak for some time and then knead it with your hands till it's soft. Squeeze out excess water from the paper mixture. At this point you can add coloring or essential oil to your mixture to give a color or nice aroma to your paper. Carefully spread the mixture on the cheese cloth. Depending on the weather it can take anywhere between an hour to two days for the paper to completely dry. Carefully peel off the dry paper.

# ALL ABOUT

# AUSTRALIAN SNUBFIN DOLPHIN

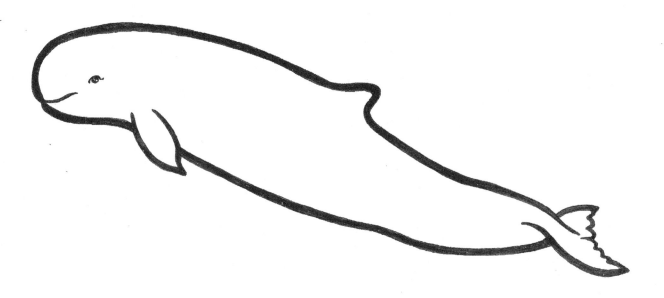

WRITE DOWN THREE FACTS ABOUT THIS ANIMAL:

1._____

_____

2._____

_____

3._____

_____

# RESEARCH & DISCOVERIES

## USE LIBRARY BOOKS, ENCYCLOPEDIAS OR THE INTERNET TO LEARN MORE.

Color the parts of the world where this animal lives.

| DRAW MY HOME | DRAW MY FOOD | DRAW MY ENEMIES |
| --- | --- | --- |
| | | |

# Reduce, Reuse, Recycle

Reusing is when we take some item that we might consider throwing away and find a way for it to be useful again. We can use the item for it's original purpose or find a new and creative way to use it. Finding a new way to use it is called repurposing. In each box draw something that can be reused or repurposed.

# MATH TIME

Use this page for math lessons & practice.

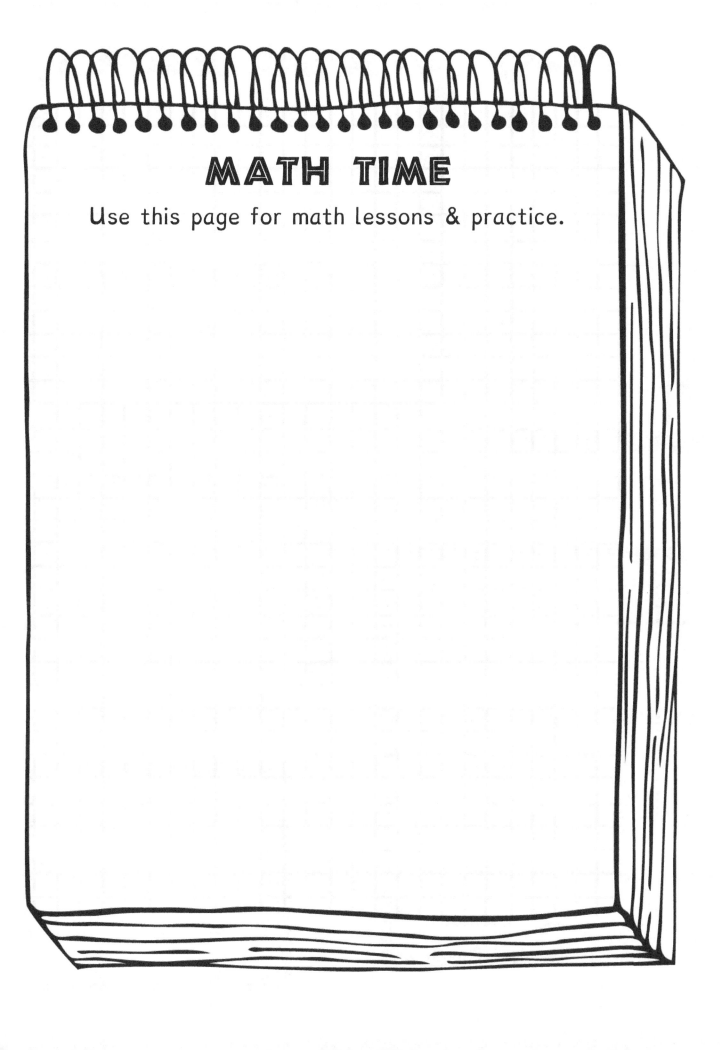

## TODAYS DATE:

\_ \_ \_ \_ \_ \_

\_ \_ \_ \_ \_ \_

\_ \_ \_ \_ \_ \_

# TO-DO LIST

1._____

2._____

3._____

4._____

# A New Day!

## How are you FEELING TODAY?

I am THANKFUL for:

Draw a Dolphin Comic:

# COLORING TIME

## Relax & Listen to an Audio Book

Today I will read for

15 30 45 60

MINUTES

READING TIME

Write and draw about what you are reading.

# BACKYARD SCIENCE
# NATURE WALK & NATURE STUDY

Draw or write about the things you see outside today.

# CREATIVE WRITING

Write a short story about these pictures.

_____

_____

_____

_____

_____

_____

_____

_____

_____

_____

_____

_____

_____

_____

_____

_____

_____

_____

_____

_____

_____

_____

# MOVIE TIME

Watch an Video about Dolphins or the Ocean!

TITLE:_____

RATING:

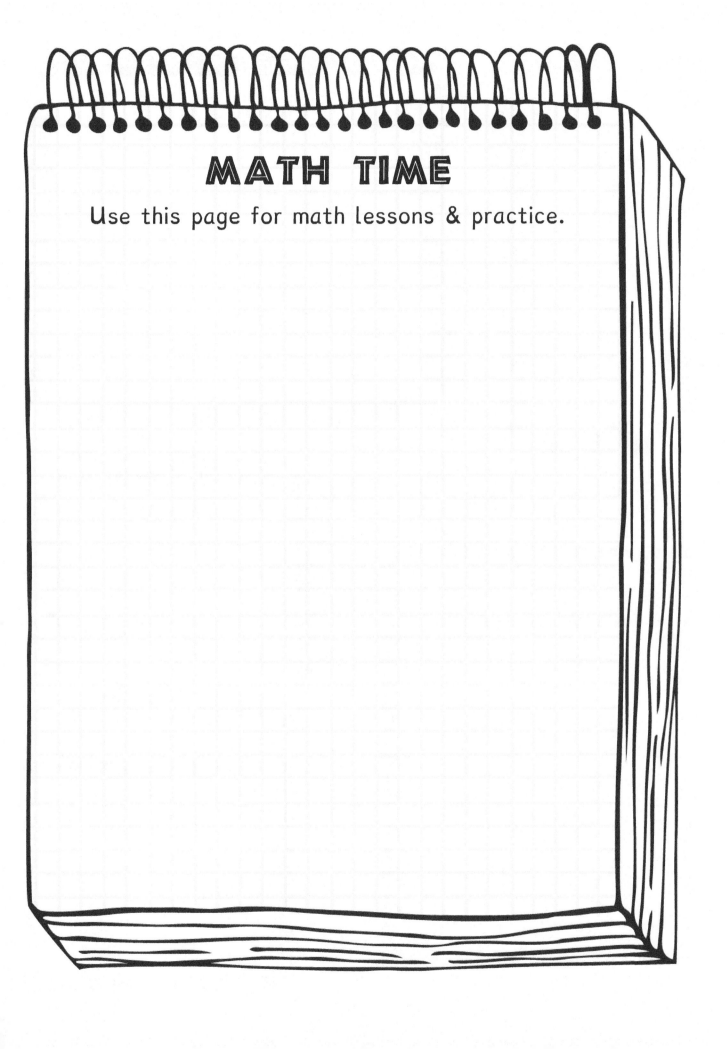

# MATH TIME

Use this page for math lessons & practice.

## TODAYS DATE:

_ _ _ _ _ _

_ _ _ _ _ _

_ _ _ _ _ _

## TO-DO LIST

1. _____

2. _____

3. _____

4. _____

# A New Day!

How are you
FEELING TODAY?

I am THANKFUL for:

Draw a Dolphin Comic:

# OCEAN LIFE DRAWING TIME

Use a step-by-step drawing book or video.

# Water conservation

Water conservation is a way of using water responsibly and reducing unnecessary usage of water. It is a way of preserving and managing fresh water resources and reducing water wastage. Conserving water is important because it keeps water pure and clean while protecting the environment. Using less water keeps more clean water in our ecosystem. It helps to keep a safe and natural environment for animals and fish.

What are some different ways to save water?

Create a poster For Water conservation aWareness

CREATE A COMIC STRIP

A B C D E F G

H I J K L M

N O P Q R S T

U V W X Y Z

a b c d e f g h

i j k l m n o p

q r s t u v w x

y z 1 2 3 4 5 6 7 8 9 0

# CURSIVE WRITING PRACTICE

# ALL ABOUT

# PANTROPICAL SPOTTED

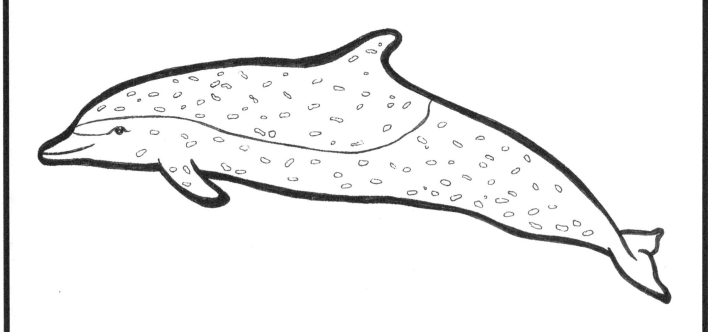

## WRITE DOWN THREE FACTS ABOUT THIS ANIMAL:

1._____

_____

2._____

_____

3._____

_____

# RESEARCH & DISCOVERIES

## USE LIBRARY BOOKS, ENCYCLOPEDIAS OR THE INTERNET TO LEARN MORE.

Color the parts of the world where this animal lives.

| DRAW MY HOME | DRAW MY FOOD | DRAW MY ENEMIES |
| --- | --- | --- |
|  |  |  |

## TODAYS DATE:

‾ ‾ ‾ ‾ ‾ ‾

‾ ‾ ‾ ‾ ‾ ‾

‾ ‾ ‾ ‾ ‾ ‾

# TO-DO LIST

1._____

2._____

3._____

4._____

# A New Day!

How are you FEELING TODAY?

I am THANKFUL for:

Draw a Dolphin Comic:

# OCEAN LIFE DRAWING TIME

Use a step-by-step drawing book or video.

**READING TIME**

Write and draw about
what you are reading.

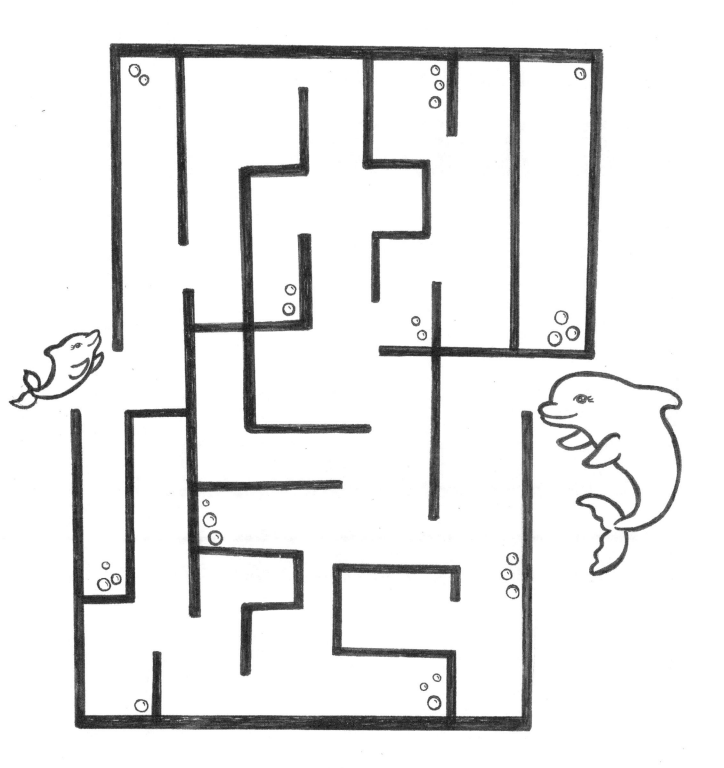

# MOVIE TIME

## Watch an Video about Dolphins or the Ocean!

TITLE:_____

RATING:

Draw Your Favorite Scenes:

# OCEAN LIFE DRAWING TIME

Use a step-by-step drawing book or video.

# South Asian river dolphin

## WRITE DOWN THREE FACTS ABOUT THIS ANIMAL:

1._____

_____

2._____

_____

3._____

_____

# RESEARCH & DISCOVERIES

## USE LIBRARY BOOKS, ENCYCLOPEDIAS OR THE INTERNET TO LEARN MORE.

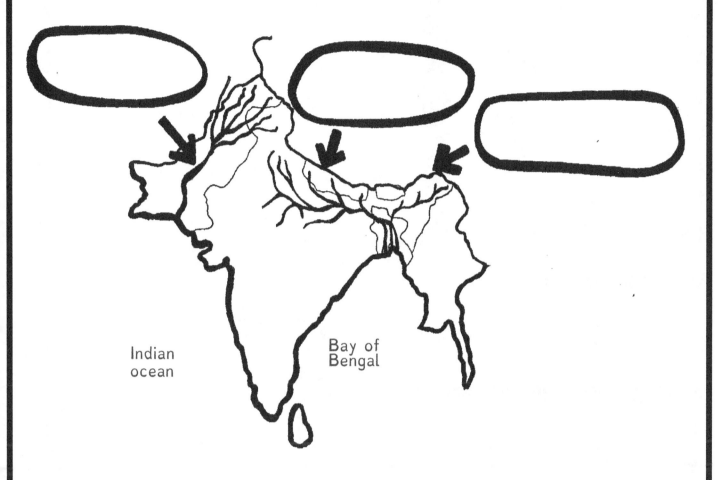

Indian ocean

Bay of Bengal

Write the names of the rivers where this animal lives.

| Draw my home | Draw my food | Draw my enemies |
| --- | --- | --- |
|  |  |  |

**TODAYS DATE:**

\_ \_ \_ \_ \_ \_

\_ \_ \_ \_ \_ \_

\_ \_ \_ \_ \_ \_

## TO-DO LIST

1._____

2._____

3._____

4._____

# A New Day!

How are you
FEELING TODAY?

I am THANKFUL for:

Draw a Dolphin Comic:

# OCEAN LIFE DRAWING TIME

Use a step-by-step drawing book or video.

Today I will
read for

15  30  45  60

MINUTES

# READING
# TIME

Write and draw about
what you are reading.

# BACKYARD SCIENCE
# NATURE WALK & NATURE STUDY

Draw or write about the things you see outside today.

# SPELLING TIME

Pick a Letter _____

Look in your homeschooling books for

words that start with this letter.

## Write ten spelling words.

1._____

2._____

3._____

4._____

5._____

6._____

7._____

8._____

9._____

10._____

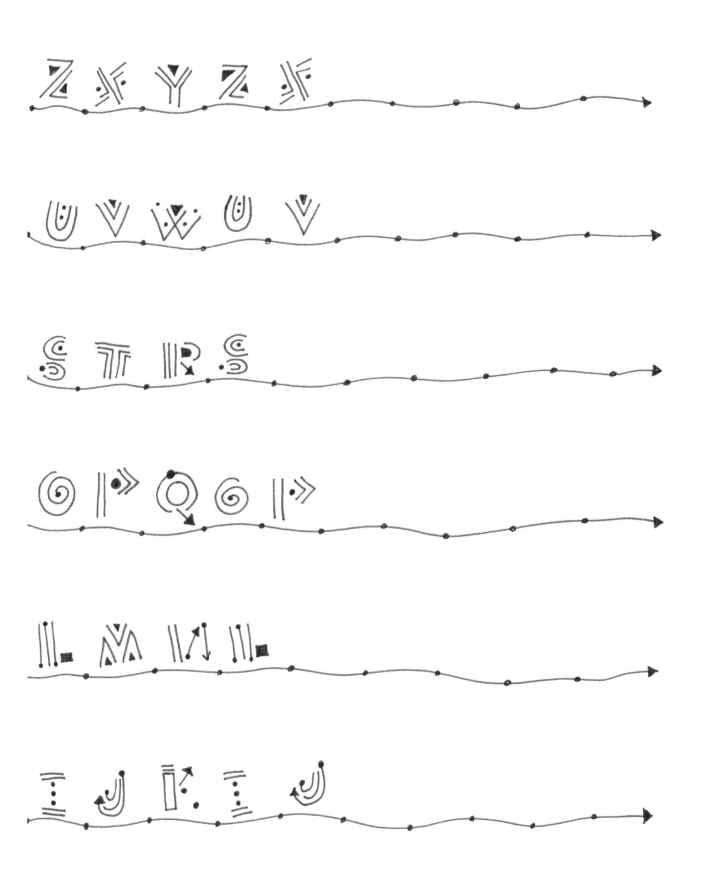

# MOVIE TIME

Watch an Video about Dolphins or the Ocean!

TITLE:_____

RATING:

Draw Your Favorite Scenes:

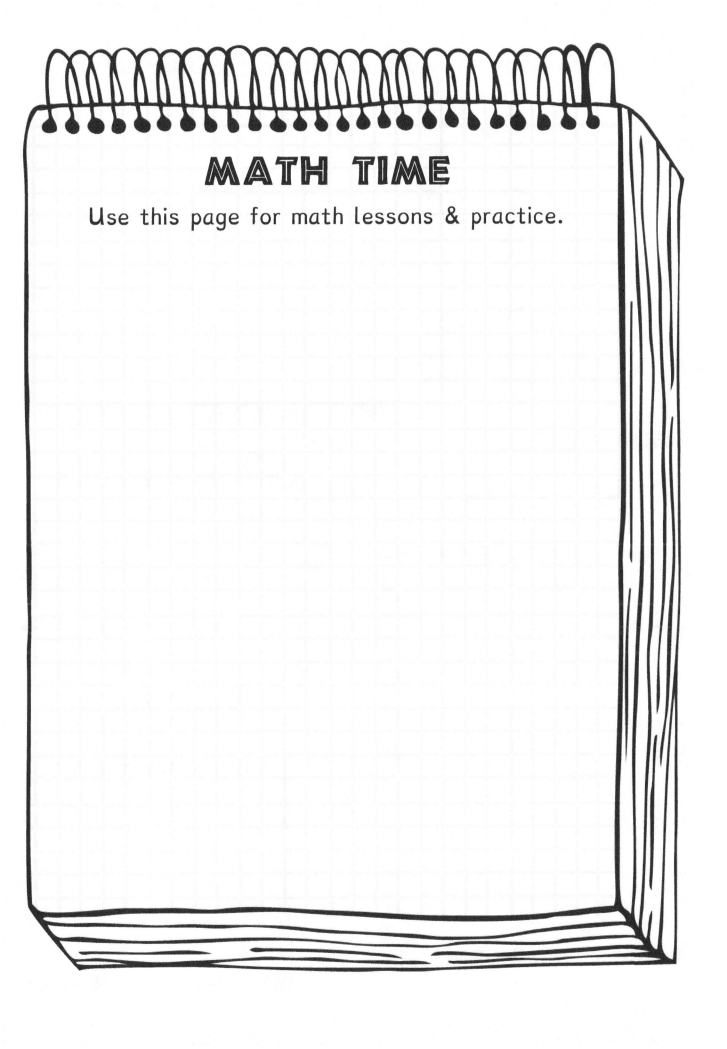

# MATH TIME

Use this page for math lessons & practice.

## TODAYS DATE:

_ _ _ _ _ _ _

_ _ _ _ _ _ _

_ _ _ _ _ _ _

## TO-DO LIST

1._____

2._____

3._____

4._____

# A New Day!

## How are you FEELING TODAY?

## I am THANKFUL for:

## Draw a Dolphin Comic:

# OCEAN LIFE DRAWING TIME

Use a step-by-step drawing book or video.

# ALL ABOUT

# SPINNER DOLPHIN

## WRITE DOWN THREE FACTS ABOUT THIS ANIMAL:

1._____

_____

2._____

_____

3._____

_____

# RESEARCH & DISCOVERIES

## USE LIBRARY BOOKS, ENCYCLOPEDIAS OR THE INTERNET TO LEARN MORE.

Color the parts of the world where this animal lives.

| DRAW MY HOME | DRAW MY FOOD | DRAW MY ENEMIES |
| --- | --- | --- |
|  |  |  |

# RainWater HarVeSting

You WiLL Need:

BucKet or a Wide bowL; rope or Waterproof tape; piece of MeSH, Net or cHeeSe cLotH; Heavy FoiL or plastic bag.

Rainwater harvesting is the collection and storage of rain. The rain water is collected from a wide surface like a roof and stored in a water tank, cistern, well or an artificial pond. Rain water can be stored and used later, for example for watering a garden. When we use water from lakes, rivers or underground sources the ground water supply is reduced, but using rainwater can replenish it! Collecting rainwater reduces floods and soil erosion, saves electricity and benefits nature in many other ways! It can also help people living in the areas with water shortage to grow food and to have enough water for their daily needs.

INSTRUCTIONS:
Cover the bucket or bowl with a mesh or a net. This is important to prevent insects from entering and also to filter away any dirt. Make a hole in the center of a piece of heavy foil or a plastic bag and cover the bucket.

Push the center down, so the water can flow towards the opening. Secure the cover with a rope or a tape. To make sure the bucket is not flipped by wind, secure it with some rocks or place it a few inches deep in the ground. Now you can
collect water and use it to water plants. You can also create a full size rainwater collection system. In addition to the parts that the small model has, it would need an overflow opening (covered with mesh,) a tap and a bigger water collection  surface.

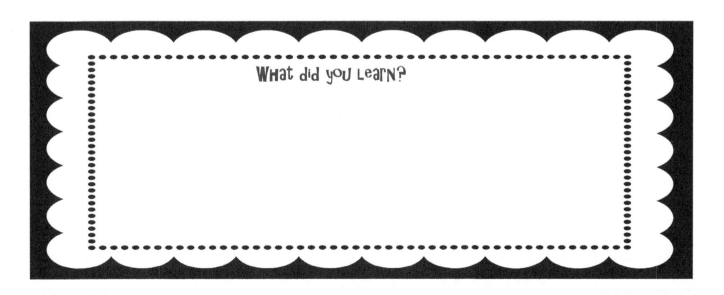

What did you Learn?

CREATE A COMIC STRIP

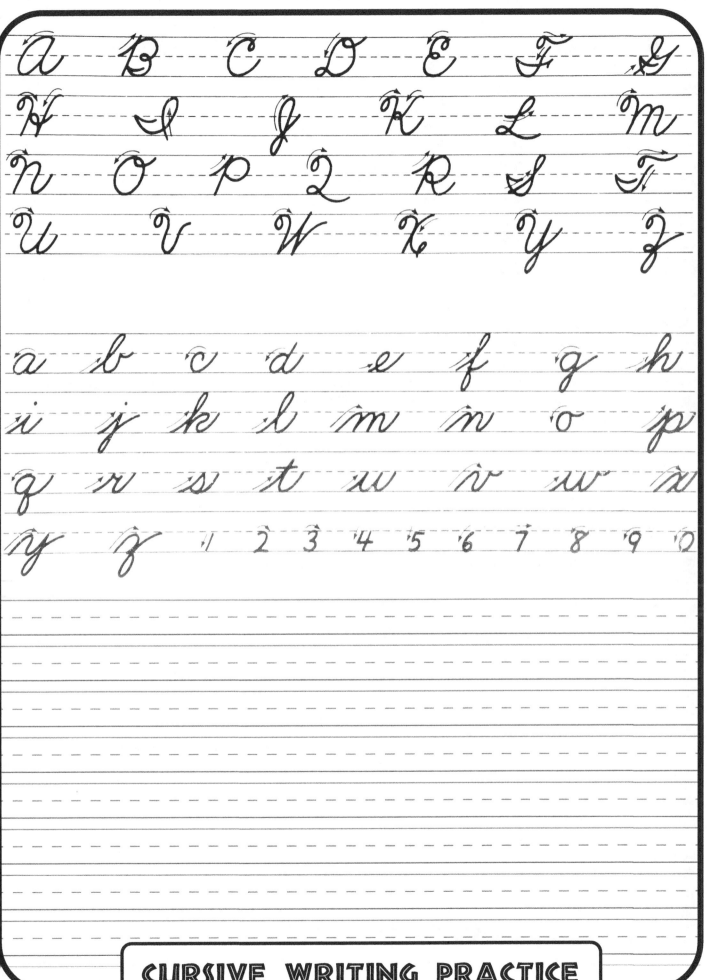

CURSIVE WRITING PRACTICE

## TODAYS DATE:

‐‐‐‐‐‐‐‐

‐‐‐‐‐‐‐‐

‐‐‐‐‐‐‐‐

## TO-DO LIST

1._____

2._____

3._____

4._____

# A New Day!

### How are you FEELING TODAY?

I am THANKFUL for:

Draw a Dolphin Comic:

Today I will
read for

15  30  45  60

MINUTES

## READING TIME

Write and draw about
what you are reading.

# COPYWORK

Copy a sentence from one of your library books.

TITLE: _____

Page#_____

_____

_____

_____

_____

_____

# DRAWING TIME

Copy an illustration from one of your books.

# COLORING TIME

## Relax & Listen to an Audio Book

# MATH TIME

Use this page for math lessons & practice.

# DRAWING TIME

## PRACTICE DRAWING DOLPHINS & SEA CREATURES

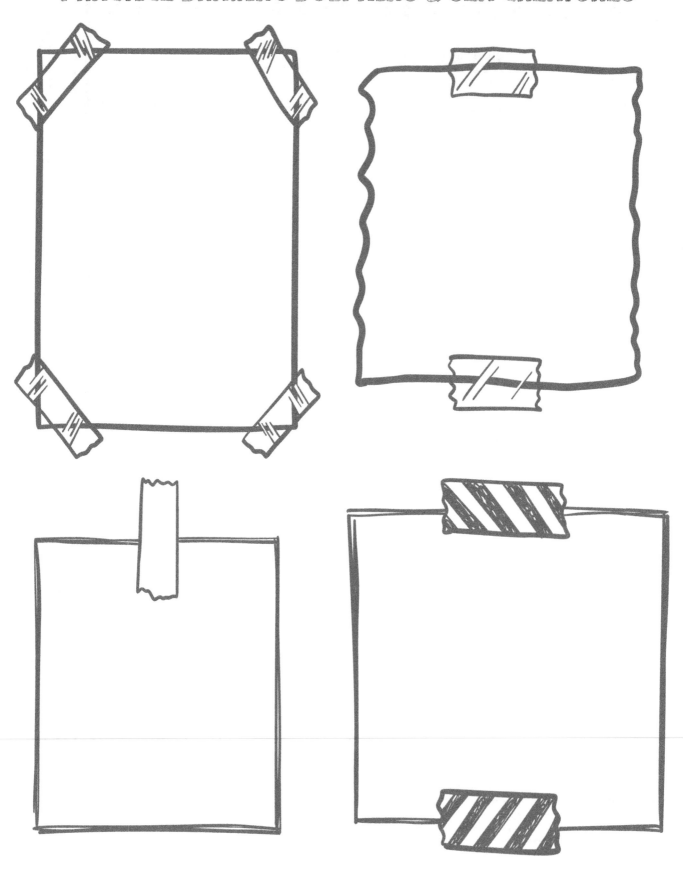

# Reduce, Reuse, Recycle

Reducing means to use less items that create waste. We can reduce the amount of waste that we create by: replacing one time use items with reusable ones; buying recycled or used things; choosing products that don't have plastic packing and buying less of unnecessary things, like plastic bags or plastic straws. In the below boxes draw some items that we can reduce in our daily use.

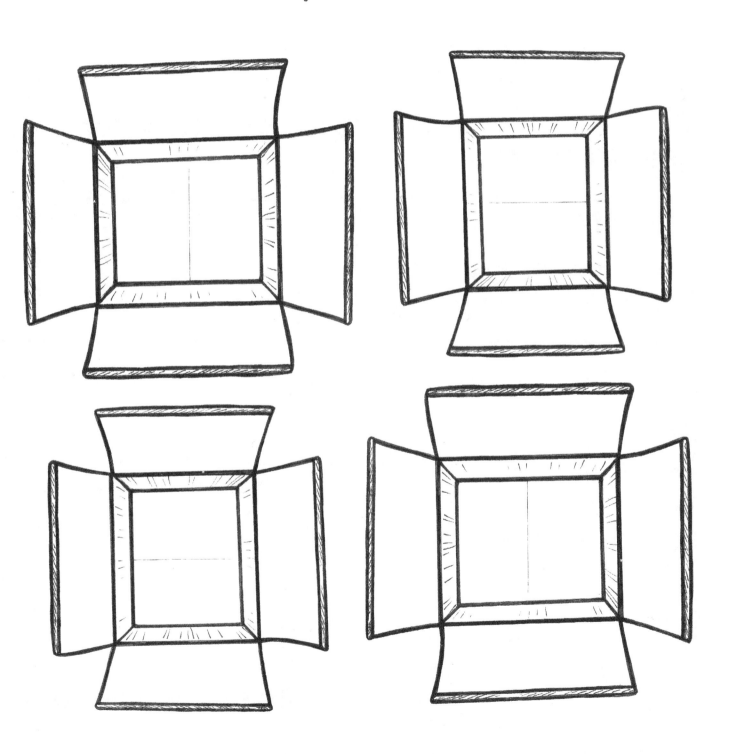

**TODAYS DATE:**

_ _ _ _ _ _ _

_ _ _ _ _ _ _

_ _ _ _ _ _ _

## TO-DO LIST

1._____

2._____

3._____

4._____

# A New Day!

How are you
**FEELING TODAY?**

I am THANKFUL for:

Draw a Dolphin Comic:

# LISTENING TIME

## CLASSICAL MUSIC, HISTORY & LITERATURE

Listen to Story of the World, an audio book

or classical music. Draw and doodle below.

I am listening to: _____

# Recycling Old Fabric

You Will Need:

Old t-Shirt or other old clothing, Scissors

Fabric is recyclable. But it is very hard to recycle, because there are so many types and varieties. So most of our old clothes just go to the landfill. Landfills are harmful for people, nature and animals.

To reduce waste we can find new uses for old clothes. If they look nice and clean—clothes can be donated. If they look old—we can use them to make crafts or household

What other crafts can you make using old clothes?

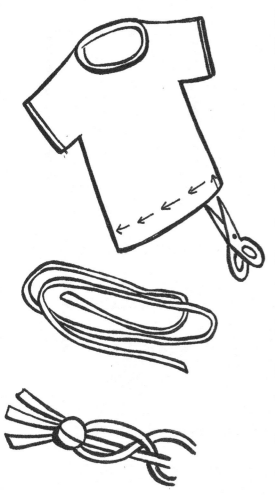

## Making a Jumping Rope
### Instructions:

There are many way to cut a shirt into a fabric "yarn". If you are using a t-shirt, start cutting from the side and go up in a spiral around the body of the shirt. This will give a long strip of fabric around one inch wide. You can use any fabric, just cut it into long strips and join them together by knots. Make three long fabric strips. Tie one end together in a big knot which will serve as a handle.

Start braiding fabric from the knot. To get the right length of rope hold both ends of the rope near your chest and see if the middle of the rope touches the floor. You can also try jumping. Once the length is right, tie the end with a big knot, so it can serve as another handle.

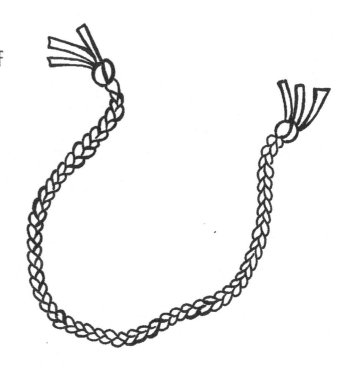

Today I will
read for

15  30  45  60

MINUTES

READING
TIME

Write and draw about
what you are reading.

Most varieties of hermit crab have long, curved, soft abdomens. The vulnerable abdomen is protected by an empty seashell carried by the crab. As the hermit crab grows in size, it must find a larger seashell and abandon the previous one.

# ALL ABOUT

# HECTORS DOLPHIN

## WRITE DOWN THREE FACTS ABOUT THIS ANIMAL:

1._____

_____

2._____

_____

3._____

_____

# RESEARCH & DISCOVERIES

## USE LIBRARY BOOKS, ENCYCLOPEDIAS OR THE INTERNET TO LEARN MORE.

Color the parts of the world where this animal lives.

| DRAW MY HOME | DRAW MY FOOD | DRAW MY ENEMIES |
| --- | --- | --- |
| | | |

**TODAYS DATE:**

_ _ _ _ _ _ _

_ _ _ _ _ _ _

_ _ _ _ _ _ _

## TO-DO LIST

1._____

2._____

3._____

4._____

# A New Day!

How are you
FEELING TODAY?

I am THANKFUL for:

Draw a Dolphin Comic:

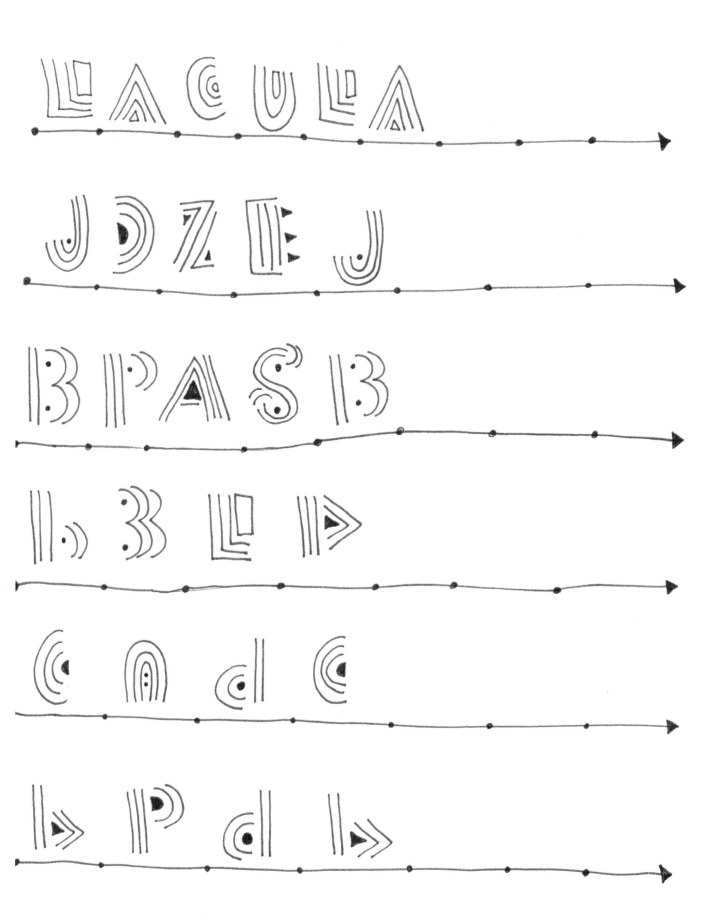

# CREATIVE WRITING

Write a short story about these pictures.

_____

_____

_____

_____

_____

_____

_____

_____

_____

_____

_____

_____

_____

_____

_____

_____

_____

_____

_____

_____

# Irrawaddy river dolphin

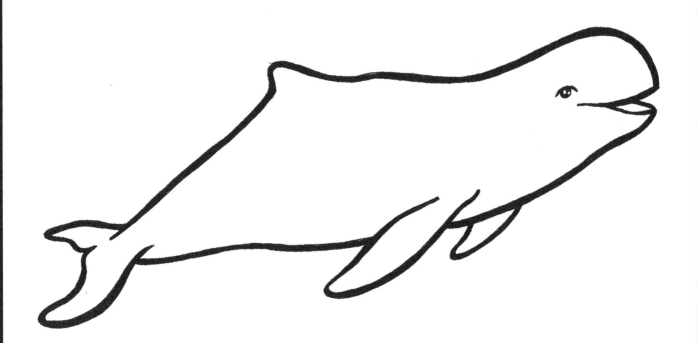

## WRITE DOWN THREE FACTS ABOUT THIS ANIMAL:

1._____

_____

2._____

_____

# RESEARCH & DISCOVERIES

## USE LIBRARY BOOKS, ENCYCLOPEDIAS OR THE INTERNET TO LEARN MORE.

Color the areas of the world where this animal lives.

| Draw my home | Draw my food | Draw my enemies |
| --- | --- | --- |
|  |  |  |

# MOVIE TIME

Watch an Video about Dolphins or the Ocean!

TITLE:_____

RATING:

# COLORING TIME

## Relax & Listen to an Audio Book

# Do It Yourself
# HOMESCHOOL
# JOURNALS

## Copyright Information

### Contact Us:

The Thinking Tree LLC

317.622.8852  PHONE (Dial +1 outside of the USA) 267.712.7889  FAX

## FunSchoolingBooks.com

Made in the USA
Las Vegas, NV
13 July 2023